GW00776043

# STUNT PLANES

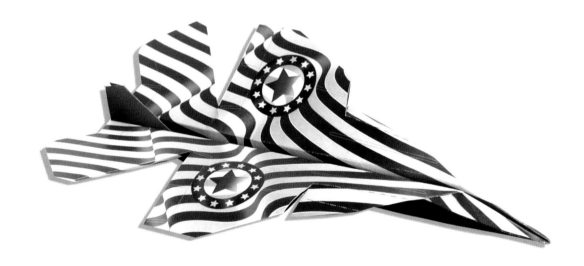

Published by Top That! Publishing plc
Tide Mill Way, Woodbridge, Suffolk, IP12 1AP, UK
www.topthatpublishing.com
Copyright © 2007 TopThat! Publishing plc
4 6 8 9 7 5 3
Printed and bound in China

# FOLDING TIPS

## BEFORE YOU BEGIN ANY OF THE PROJECTS IN THIS BOOK, HERE ARE SOME HELPFUL TIPS THAT WILL MAKE YOUR FOLDING EASIER:

- *Before you start folding, make sure your paper is the correct shape.*
- *Fold on a flat surface, like a table or a book.*
- *Make your folds and cuts neat and accurate.*
- *Crease your folds into place by running your thumbnail along them.*
- *Carefully score along the marked lines using safety scissors and a ruler. This will make folding easier, especially as the lines become obscured towards the end of the model-making.*

## SYMBOLS AND BASIC FOLDING PROCEDURES

*These symbols show the direction in which paper should be folded.*
*Although you won't need all of these folds in this book, you can use them to create your own planes.*

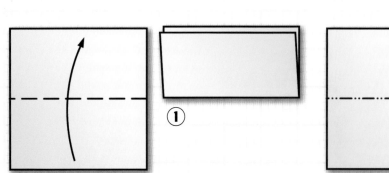

**1. VALLEY FOLD (FOLD IN FRONT)**

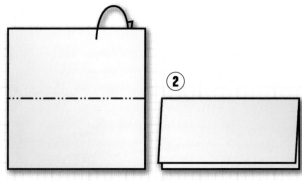

**2. MOUNTAIN FOLD (FOLD BEHIND)**

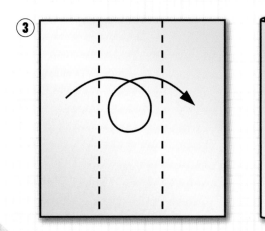

**3. FOLD OVER AND OVER**

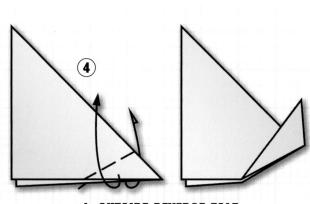

**4. OUTSIDE REVERSE FOLD**

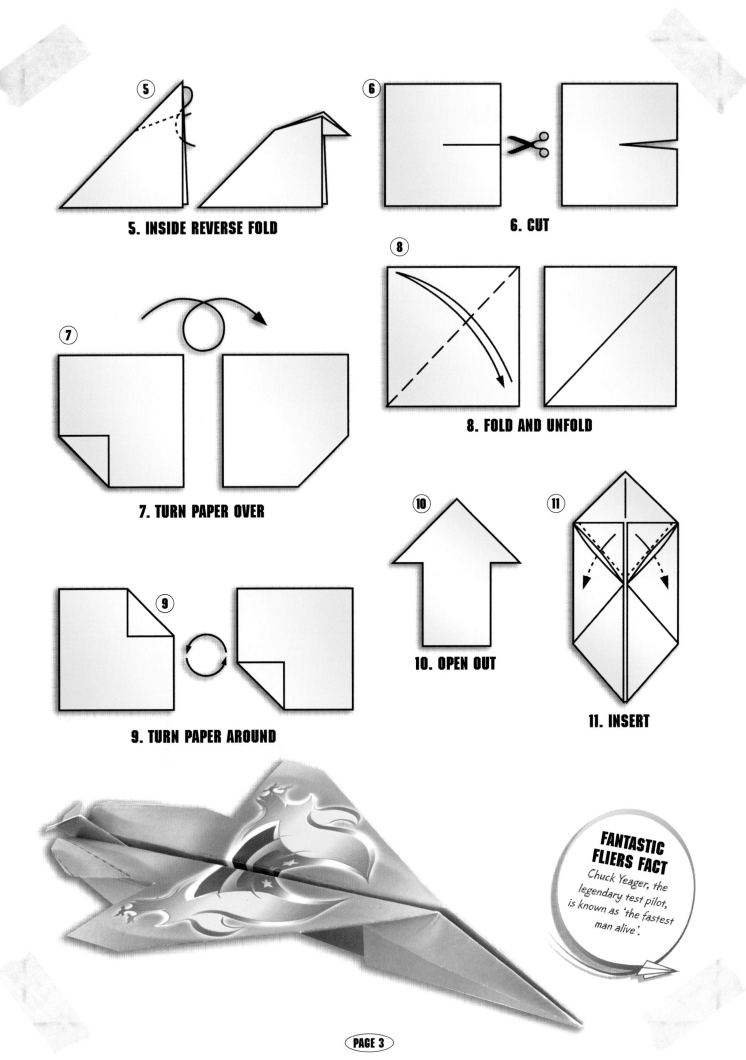

5. INSIDE REVERSE FOLD

6. CUT

7. TURN PAPER OVER

8. FOLD AND UNFOLD

9. TURN PAPER AROUND

10. OPEN OUT

11. INSERT

**FANTASTIC FLIERS FACT**
Chuck Yeager, the legendary test pilot, is known as 'the fastest man alive'.

# RADICAL ROLLER

## MAKE THIS STUNNING BARREL-ROLLING PLANE IN A FEW SIMPLE STEPS.
## USE THE PRINTED PAGE NUMBERED 1 AT THE BACK OF THIS BOOK.

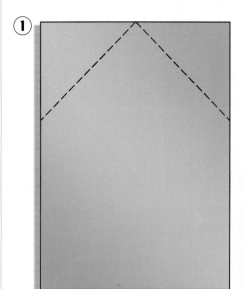

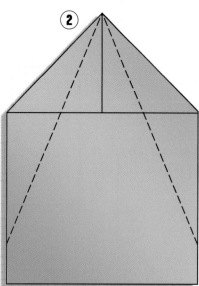

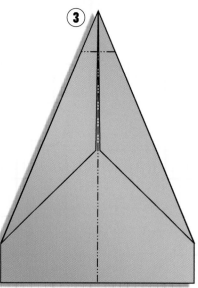

**1.** Hold the page pattern-side down. Do a valley fold along the right- and left-hand corners along the dotted line, as shown.

**2.** Using the longer dotted lines as your guide, do another valley fold along the right- and left-hand sides. Make sure you press down firmly to get a neat crease.

**3.** To form the plane's nose, do a mountain fold along the dashed edge, as shown. Make another mountain fold along the centre of the plane. Again, make sure you press firmly enough to make a neat crease.

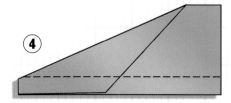

**4.** Make a valley fold along the body of the plane following the dotted lines as a guide.

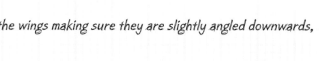

**5.** Open out the wings making sure they are slightly angled downwards, as shown.

To fly your Radical Roller, hold it underneath between your thumb and forefinger about 10 cm from the front, and throw it fast into the air.

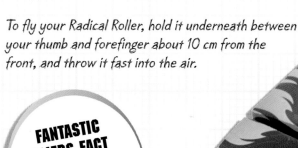

**FANTASTIC FLIERS FACT**

The first display by the British Red Arrows was on May 6th, 1965.

# BRILLIANT BOOMERANG

## THIS AMAZING STUNT PLANE RETURNS TO BASE ON ITS OWN.
## USE THE PRINTED PAGE NUMBERED 2 AT THE BACK OF THIS BOOK.

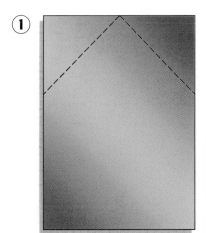

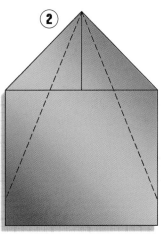

**1.** Hold the page pattern-side down. Do a valley fold along the right- and left-hand corners along the dotted line as shown.

**2.** Using the longer dotted lines as your guide, do another valley fold along the right- and left-hand sides making sure you press down firmly to get a neat crease.

**3.** Using valley folds, bring the two bottom corners up to form a V-shape.

**4.** Take the bottom V-shape piece and fold down along the dashed line with a mountain fold, as shown.

**5.** Fold the plane in half, using a mountain fold along the centre dashed line.

**6.** Fold the wings along the dotted line, making sure that you adjust their angle upward.

To fly your Brilliant Boomerang, hold it underneath between your forefinger and thumb, about 7 cm from the front. Throw it slowly, and it will curve around in a loop to return to where it began.

### FANTASTIC FLIERS FACT
The Canadian Snowbirds stunt team has been seen by over 90 million people in the last 20 years.

# LOOPY LOOPER

## LOOP THE LOOP WITH THIS CRAZY STUNT MACHINE.
## USE THE PRINTED PAGE NUMBERED 3 AT THE BACK OF THIS BOOK.

①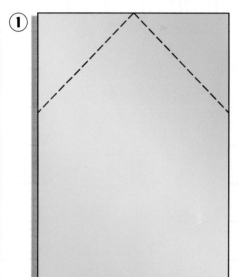

②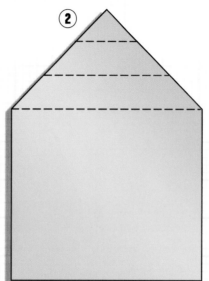

③

**1.** Hold the page pattern-side down. Do a valley fold along the right- and left-hand corners along the dotted line as shown.

**2.** Fold down the pointed tip first along the top dotted line, and then along the second dotted line using valley folds. Repeat this along the third dotted line to fold it down further, as shown.

**3.** Use a mountain fold to fold it down the centre along the dashed line, as shown.

④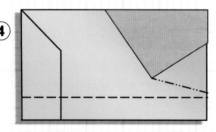

**4.** Take a pair of scissors and carefully cut along the solid line, making sure to cut through both sides of the plane to make a cut-out V shape. Fold the wings down before folding up the tips at the tail end.

 ⑤

**5.** Before you fly your plane, gently angle the wings upward and the tail fins upwards also.

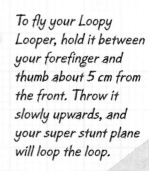

**FANTASTIC FLIERS FACT**
The Red Arrows often fly as low as 30 metres above the ground.

To fly your Loopy Looper, hold it between your forefinger and thumb about 5 cm from the front. Throw it slowly upwards, and your super stunt plane will loop the loop.

# DARING DART

## THIS FAST AND FURIOUS DART-LIKE PLANE WILL STREAK THROUGH THE AIR LIKE LIGHTNING. USE THE PRINTED PAGE NUMBERED 4 AT THE BACK OF THIS BOOK.

①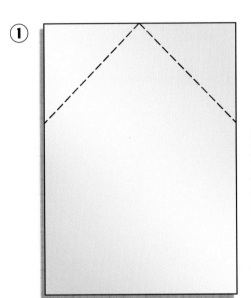

②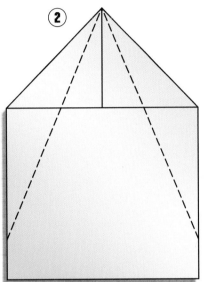

③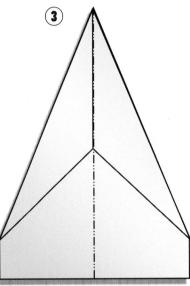

**1.** Hold the page pattern-side down. Do a valley fold along the right- and left-hand corners along the dotted line as shown.

**2.** Using the longer dotted lines as your guide, do another valley fold along the right- and left-hand sides. Make sure you press down firmly to get a neat crease.

**3.** Using a mountain fold, fold the plane in half along the centre dashed line.

**4.** To form the wings, valley fold both the left- and right-hand side of the plane along the long dashed lines, as shown. Remember to press firmly to ensure a neatly creased edge.

④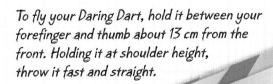

**5.** Do a valley fold on the wing tips along the dotted lines.

⑤

To fly your Daring Dart, hold it between your forefinger and thumb about 13 cm from the front. Holding it at shoulder height, throw it fast and straight.

### FANTASTIC FLIERS FACT
The most helicopter spins in the skysurfing position record is 64 in 20 seconds by Englishman Chris Gauge in 1999.

# SUPER SPINNER

## THIS SUPER SPINNING STUNT PLANE WOULD MAKE ANY PILOT DIZZY.
## USE THE PRINTED PAGE NUMBERED 5 AT THE BACK OF THIS BOOK.

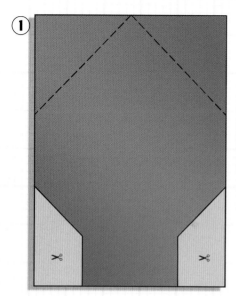

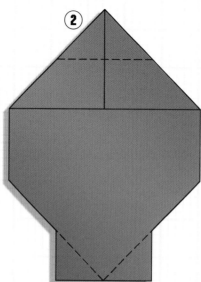

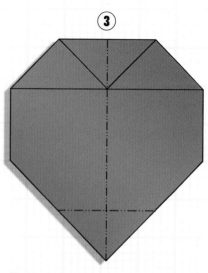

**1.** Hold the page pattern-side down. Do a valley fold along the right- and left-hand corners along the dotted line as shown. Use a pair of scissors to carefully cut out the bottom corners along the solid line.

**2.** Take the top pointed edge and make a valley fold along the dotted line, as shown. Then do another two valley folds along the bottom dotted lines to form a V shape.

**3.** Take the bottom V-shaped piece and, using a mountain fold along the dashed line, turn it behind the body. Then fold the plane along the centre dashed line using a mountain fold.

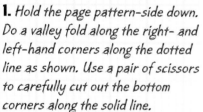

**4.** Create the pointed nose end by folding each side with a valley fold along the dotted lines, as shown. Make sure you press firmly to create a neatly creased edge

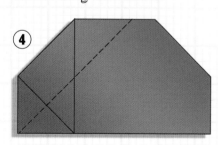

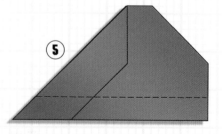

**5.** To make the wings, fold down each side along the dotted line using a valley fold. Again, press firmly to create a neat edge.

**6.** Before flying your plane, adjust the wings up slightly.

To fly your plane, hold it between your thumb and forefinger about 10 cm from the front. Throw it quite fast and high to make it perform a spiral-like spin before gently gliding to the ground.

### FANTASTIC FLIERS FACT
The US Navy 'Blue Angels' were named after a famous nightclub in New York.

# STUNT SPINNER

## THIS AMAZING PLANE PERFORMS SOME STUNNING SPINS.
## USE THE PRINTED PAGE NUMBERED 6 AT THE BACK OF THIS BOOK.

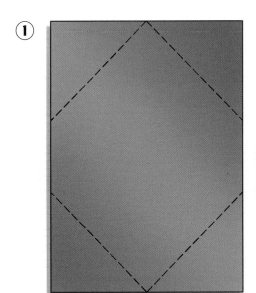

**1.** Hold the page pattern-side down. Do a valley fold along the right- and left-hand corners along the dotted line as shown.

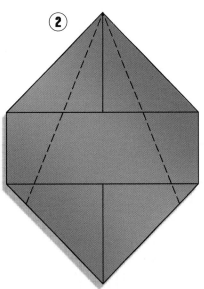

**2.** Fold in the outer edges along the dotted line to form two valley folds.

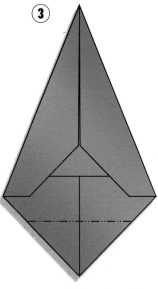

**3.** Take the pointed tip and fold it back on itself in a mountain fold.

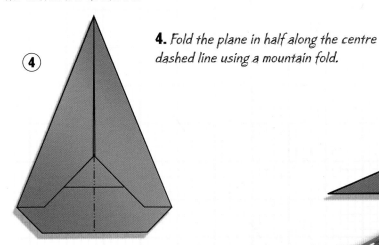

**4.** Fold the plane in half along the centre dashed line using a mountain fold.

**5.** Fold down the wings using a valley fold on each side.

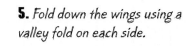
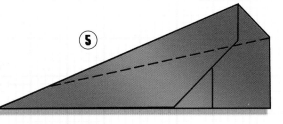

To fly your model, hold it at the tail end. Throw it high up and gently. Watch it spin!

### FANTASTIC FLIERS FACT
The Blue Angels fly six F/A-18 Hornets in formation.

# SUPER SWOOPER

## THIS INCREDIBLE BIRD-LIKE PLANE SWOOPS AND CLIMBS.
## USE THE PRINTED PAGE NUMBERED 7 AT THE BACK OF THIS BOOK.

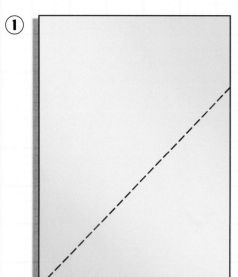

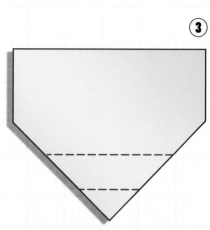

**1.** Hold the page pattern-side down. Take the bottom right-hand corner and fold it diagonally upwards in a valley fold, as shown.

**2.** Fold the bottom left-hand corner point upwards in a valley fold to create a large V shape.

**3.** Take the bottom point and fold it upwards along the bottom dotted line in a valley fold. Now, make a valley fold on the second dotted line. As you bring up the second fold, gently tuck in the small triangle-shaped tip into the back pocket.

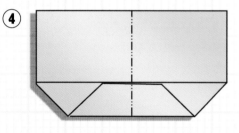

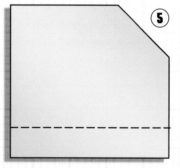

**4.** Fold the plane in half by making a mountain fold along the centre dotted line. Make sure that you press firmly to create a neat edge.

**5.** Make the two wings by using valley folds to bring down the right- and left-hand sides. Again, press firmly on the edges.

Before you fly your Super Swooper, angle the wings slightly upwards. Hold it about 5 cm from the front and throw it gently angled downwards.

**FANTASTIC FLIERS FACT**

Stunt manoeuvres include loops, figure-of-eights, rolls and tail slides.

# BARREL ROLL BEAUTY

## THIS PLANE IS SUPER SPEEDY AND YET SIMPLE TO MAKE!
## USE THE PRINTED PAGE NUMBERED 8 AT THE BACK OF THIS BOOK.

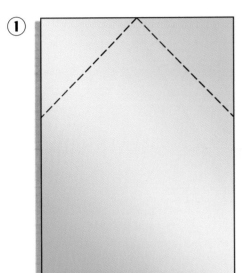

**1.** Hold the page pattern-side down. Using valley folds, bend in the two top corners.

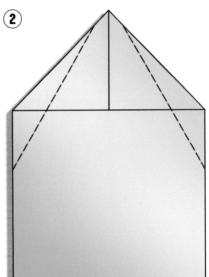

**2.** Make two valley folds along the diagonal dotted lines.

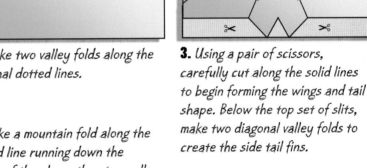

**3.** Using a pair of scissors, carefully cut along the solid lines to begin forming the wings and tail shape. Below the top set of slits, make two diagonal valley folds to create the side tail fins.

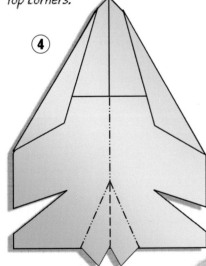

**4.** Make a mountain fold along the dashed line running down the centre of the plane, then two valley folds either side of this line. Fold the wings over. Then form a short valley fold between the two diagonal mountain folds at the rear of the plane.

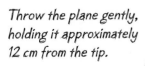

**5.** Now carefully cut along the solid lines on the wings and make valley folds along the dotted lines, as shown.

Throw the plane gently, holding it approximately 12 cm from the tip.

### FANTASTIC FLIERS FACT
Capable of flying at Mach 2, the YF-22 Raptor is one of the fastest planes.

# SPIRALLING STRIKE FIGHTER

### MAKE THIS STUNNING STRIKE FIGHTER IN MINUTES.
### USE THE PRINTED PAGE NUMBERED 9 AT THE BACK OF THIS BOOK.

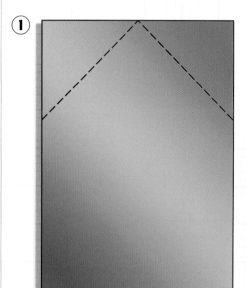

**1.** Hold the page pattern-side down. Using valley folds, fold in the top two corners.

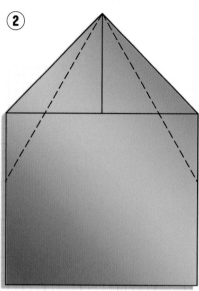

**2.** Make two more valley folds along the two diagonal dotted lines.

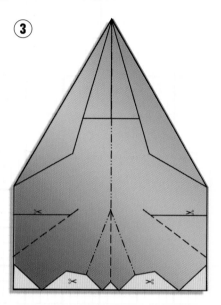

**3.** Using scissors, cut along the solid lines around the tail and wings. Make a mountain fold along the dashed line running down the centre of the plane. Form a short valley fold between the two diagonal mountain folds at the rear of the plane. Now make horizontal cuts on each rear wing and fold the flaps under each slit along the dotted lines as shown.

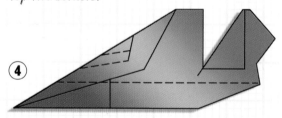

**4.** Make valley folds along the dotted lines on the wings, as shown. Cut along the diagonal solid lines. Using more valley folds, form the front wings on either side of the plane.

Throw the plane gently, holding it approximately 10 cm from the tip.

**FANTASTIC FLIERS FACT**
In the movie 'Octopussy', a 4 metre long Bede Acrostar jet is used by James Bond to evade a heat-seeking missile.

# NIFTY NOSEDIVER

## FOLLOW THESE EASY STEPS AND SEE YOUR SUPERSONIC JET FLY!
## USE THE PRINTED PAGE NUMBERED 10 AT THE BACK OF THIS BOOK.

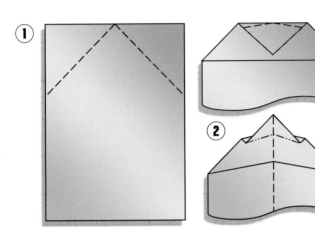

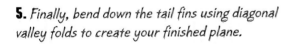

**1.** Hold the page pattern-side down. Fold in the top two corners using valley folds.

**2.** Now fold the pointed tip towards you using a valley fold along the straight dotted line. Next, make two mountain folds along the diagonal dashed lines by folding the pointed tip back on itself. Firmly fold the plane down its centre, using a valley fold, ensuring that the folds in the pointed tip stay securely tucked in place.

**5.** Finally, bend down the tail fins using diagonal valley folds to create your finished plane.

Holding your plane approximately 5 cm from the tip of the nose cone, pinch the underside of the wings together and allow your jet to gently glide out of your hand.

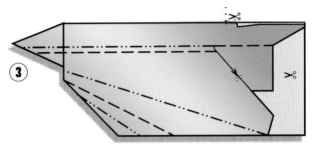

**3.** Using a pair of scissors, carefully cut out the tail and wing shapes using the solid lines as a guide. Make the valley and mountain folds on both sides of the plane's body as indicated by the dotted and dashed lines. Now, make the valley and mountain folds on both wing sections in the same way.

**4.** Next, using two more mountain folds, bend the tail into shape along the dashed lines and back up through the tail.

### FANTASTIC FLIERS FACT
The F-16 Thunderbird team's most famous formation is the flying diamond.

# ASTOUNDING U-TURNER

## THIS PLANE IS FULL OF CUNNING MANOEUVRES – WHY NOT TAKE IT FOR A SPIN?
## USE THE PRINTED PAGE NUMBERED 11 AT THE BACK OF THIS BOOK.

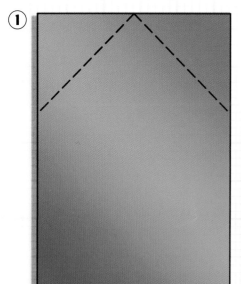

**1.** Hold the page pattern-side down. Using valley folds, fold the top corners along the dotted lines.

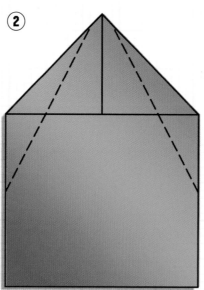

**2.** Make two more valley folds along the diagonal dotted lines.

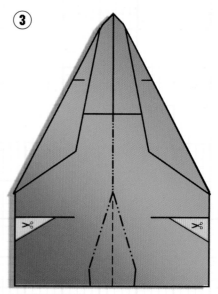

**3.** Cut along all the solid lines around the wing area as shown. Then, make a mountain fold along the dashed line running down the centre of the plane. Form a short valley fold between the two diagonal mountain folds at the rear.

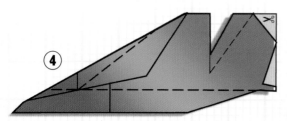

**4.** Next, cut along the solid lines around the tail area. Form the wings and tail fins by making the remaining valley folds on both sides of the plane's body as indicated by the dotted lines.

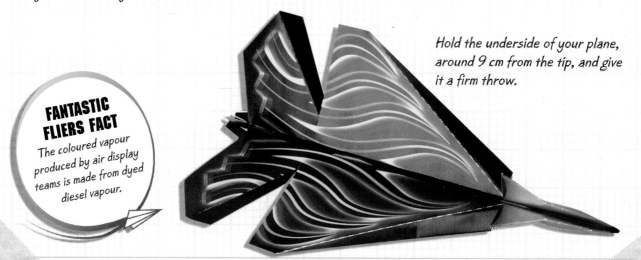

Hold the underside of your plane, around 9 cm from the tip, and give it a firm throw.

### FANTASTIC FLIERS FACT
The coloured vapour produced by air display teams is made from dyed diesel vapour.

# WHIZZING WEAVER

## THE SENSATIONAL JET IS SUPER SPEEDY AND EASY TO MAKE.
## USE THE PRINTED PAGE NUMBERED 12 AT THE BACK OF THIS BOOK.

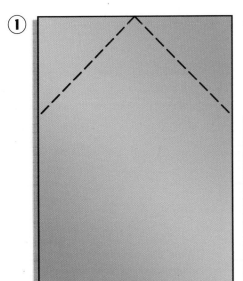

**1.** Hold the page pattern-side down. Using valley folds, fold the top corners along the dotted lines.

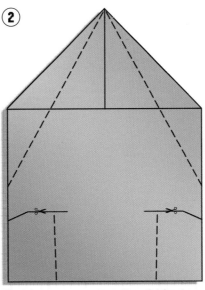

**2.** Make two more valley folds along the diagonal dotted lines. Using a pair of scissors, carefully cut along the solid lines. Now fold in the two flaps along the dotted lines.

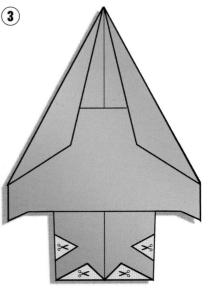

**3.** Using a pair of scissors, carefully cut away the four triangles to shape the tail fins.

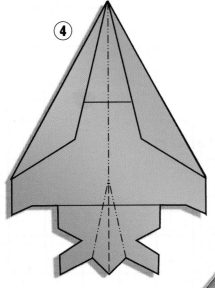

**4.** Fold in the tail along the vertical fold lines. Now make mountain folds along the three dashed lines running down the centre of the plane. Make sure you form a short valley fold between the two diagonal mountain folds at the rear, keeping the tail pieces tucked inside as you fold.

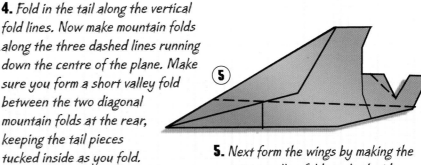

**5.** Next form the wings by making the remaining valley folds on both sides of the plane's body. Finish the tail with diagonal folds.

Grip the underside of your plane, approximately 9 cm from the tip, and throw.

### FANTASTIC FLIERS FACT
The world's only jet-powered biplane was piloted by Jimmy Franklin, who walked on its wings.

# CRAZY LOOPER

## MAKE THIS CRAZY LOOPER PLANE IN FIVE SIMPLE STAGES.
## USE THE PRINTED PAGE NUMBERED 13 AT THE BACK OF THIS BOOK.

①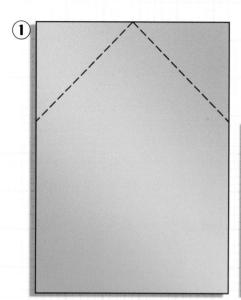

②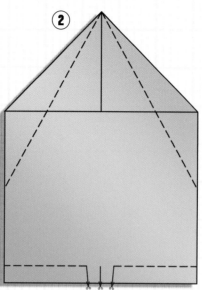

③

**1.** Hold the page pattern-side down. Fold the two top corners towards you using valley folds along the dotted lines.

**2.** Using valley folds, fold along the diagonal dotted lines. Now, using a pair of scissors, carefully cut along the three solid lines as shown, and fold along the horizontal dotted lines on either side of the cuts.

**3.** Now cut along the diagonal solid lines to help form a wing shape. Below the cuts, make two vertical valley folds and keep these flaps firmly folded in for the remaining stages.

④

**4.** Make a valley fold along the dashed line running down the centre of the plane. Form a short valley fold between the two diagonal folds at the rear of the plane.

⑤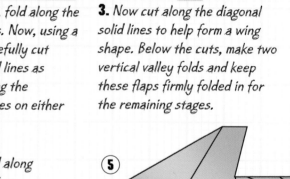

**5.** Form each wing by making valley folds on either side of the plane. To complete the tail area, fold along the lines as shown.

Hold the plane between your thumb and forefinger, approximately 9 cm from the tip, and throw it firmly.

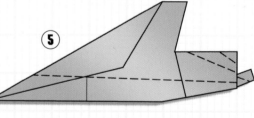

**FANTASTIC FLIERS FACT**
In 1941, the W1, designed by Frank Whittle, became the first turbojet to fly in Britain.

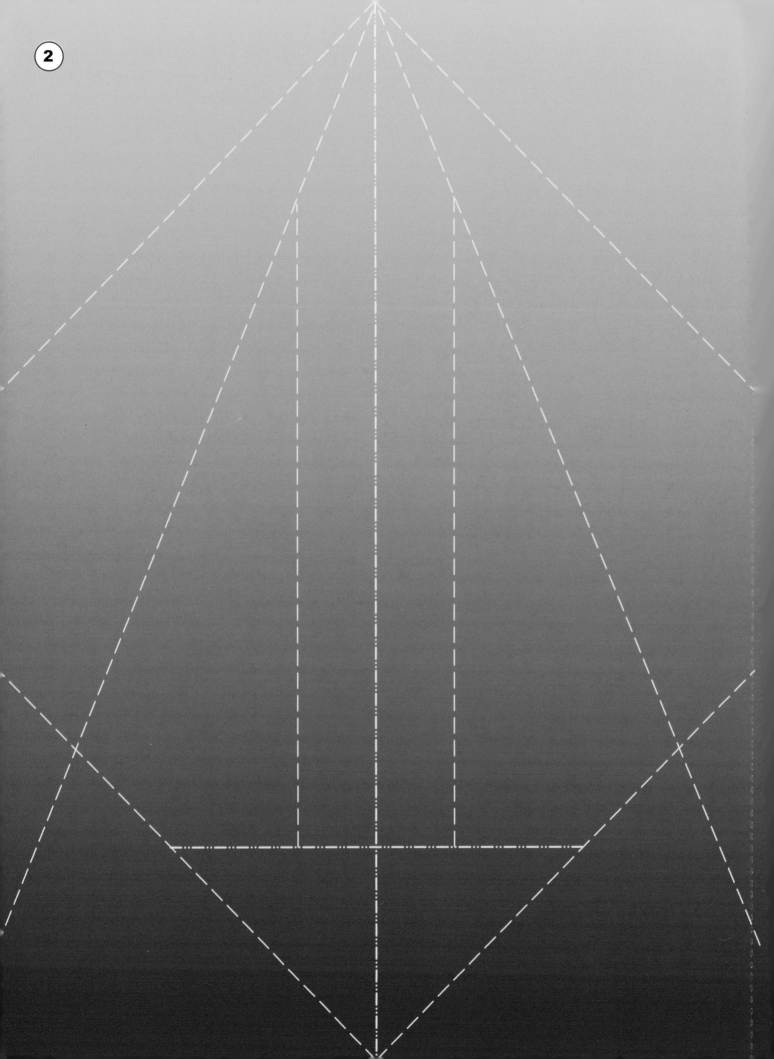

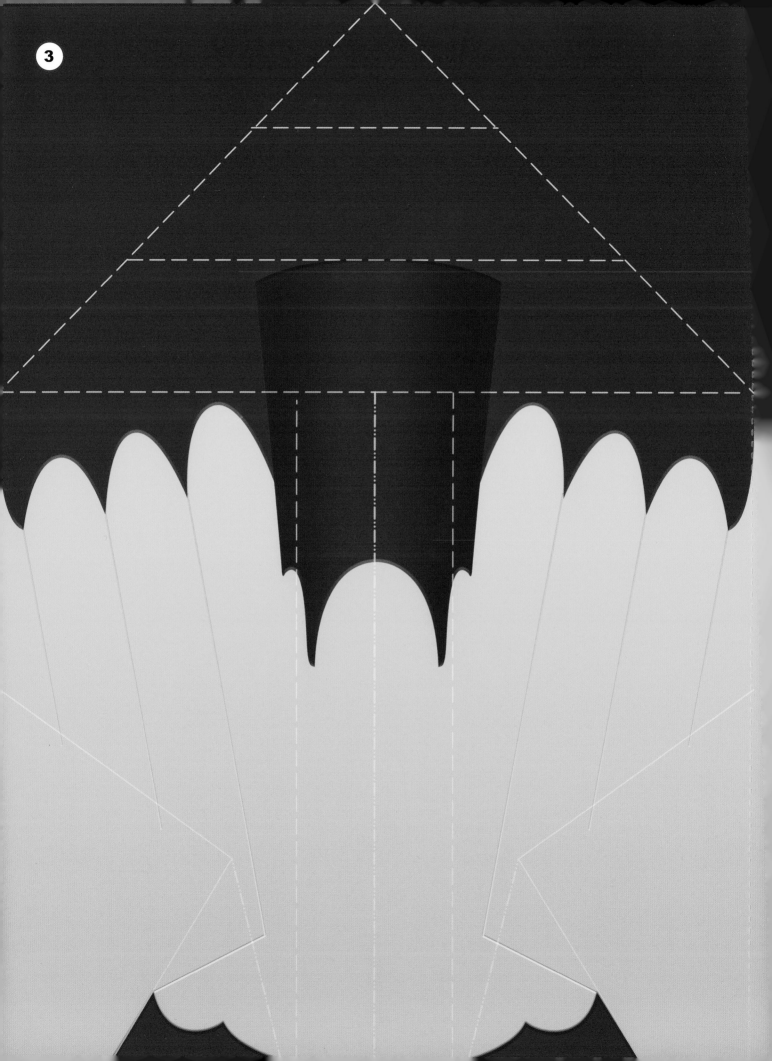

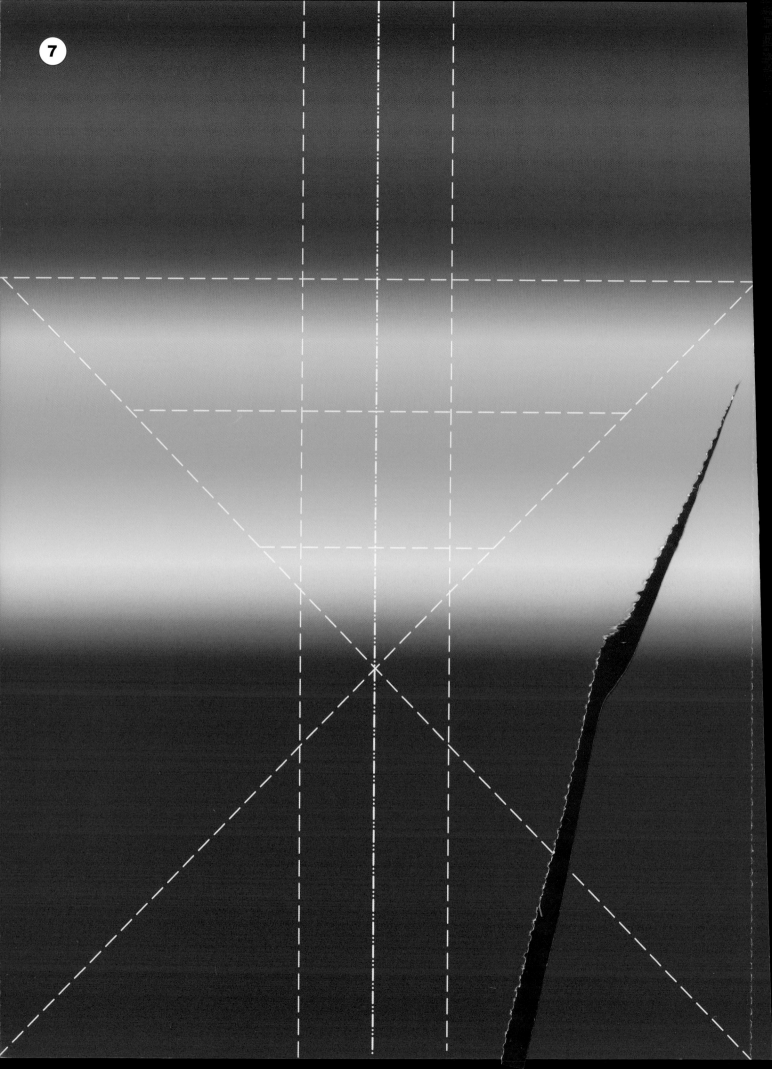

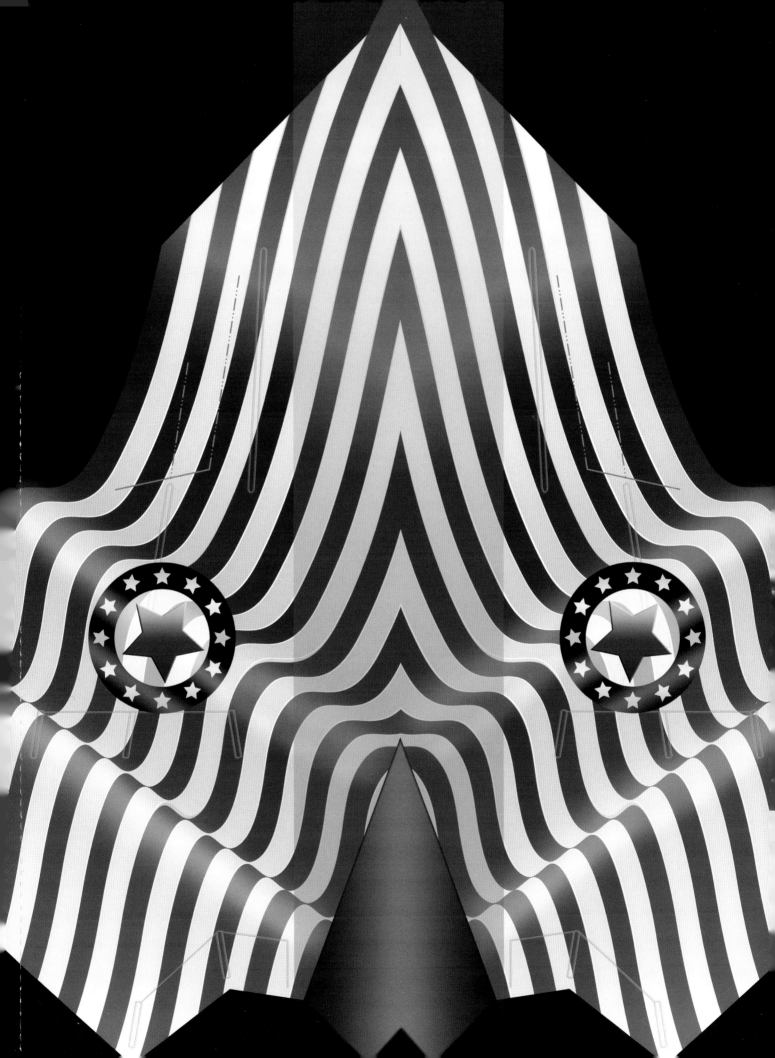

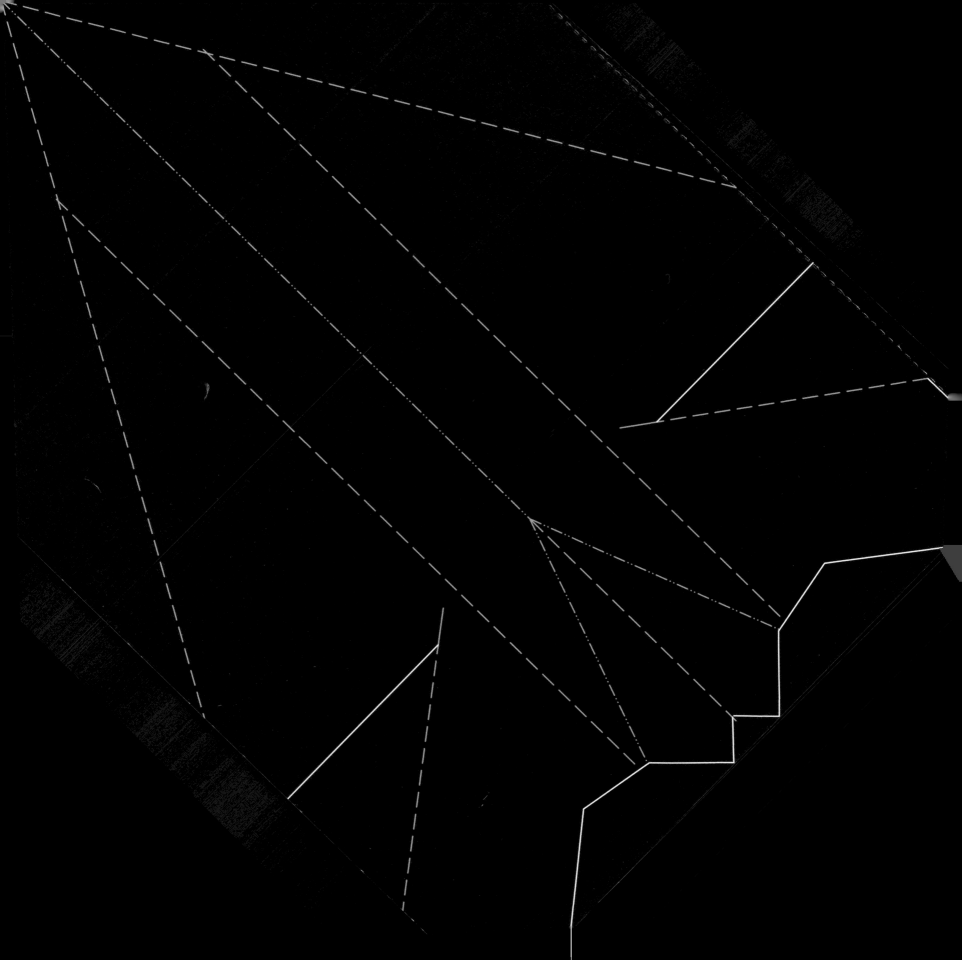

12

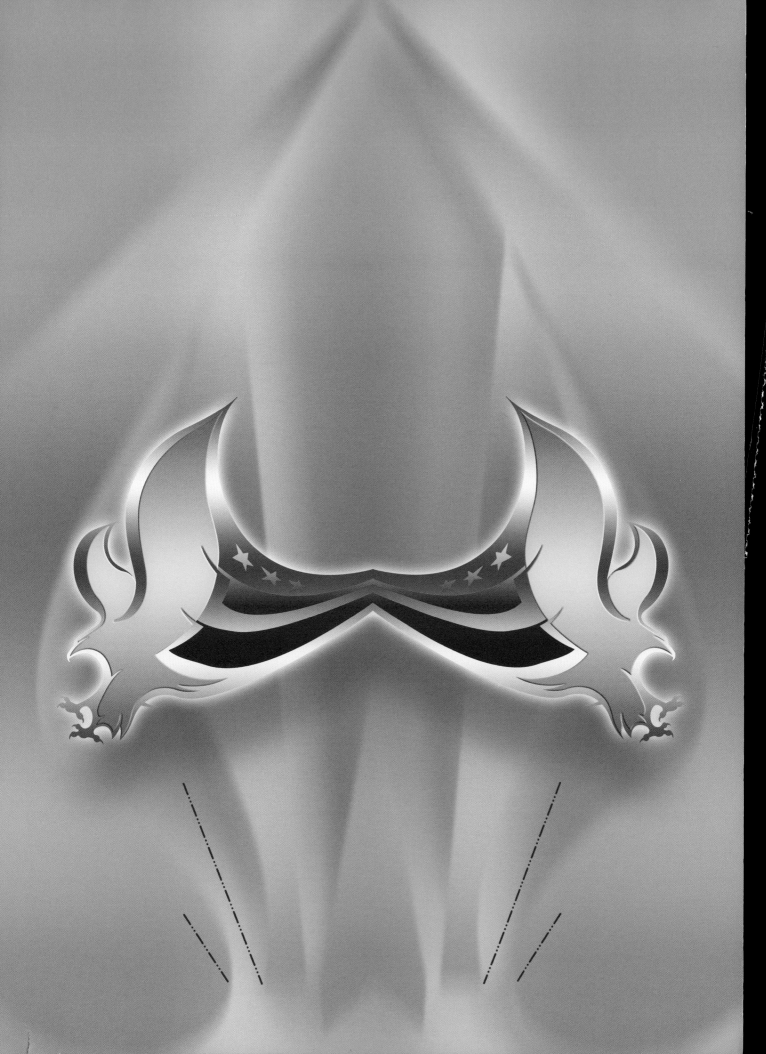

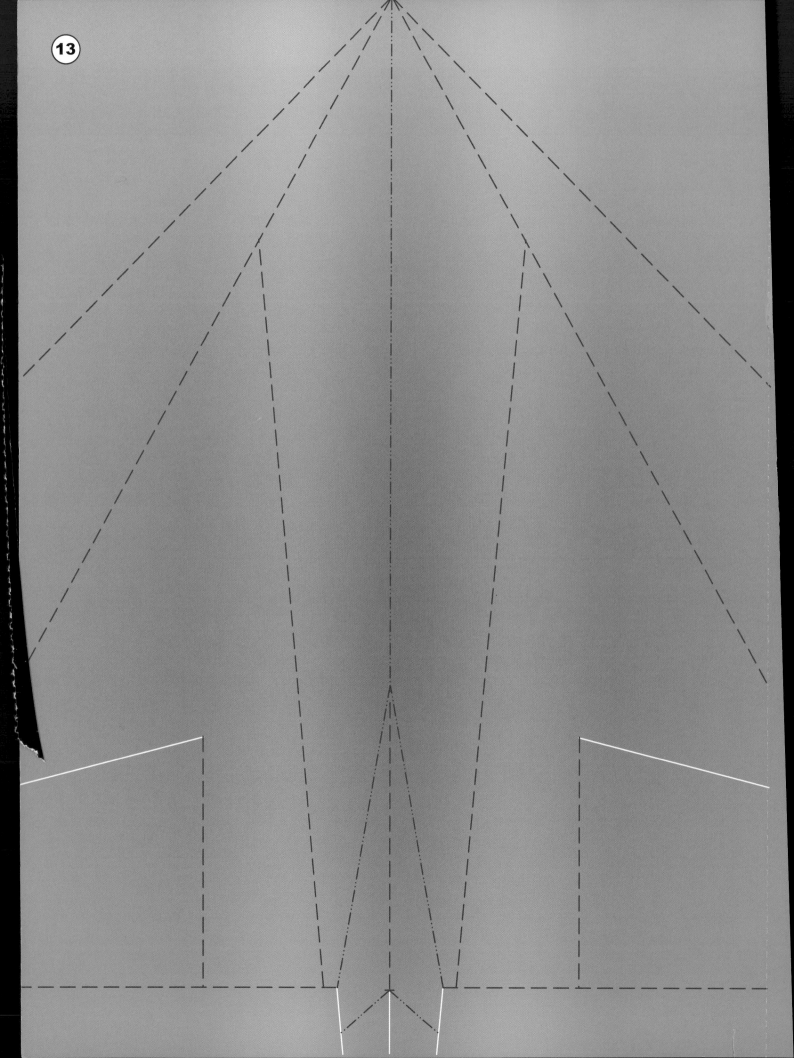

13

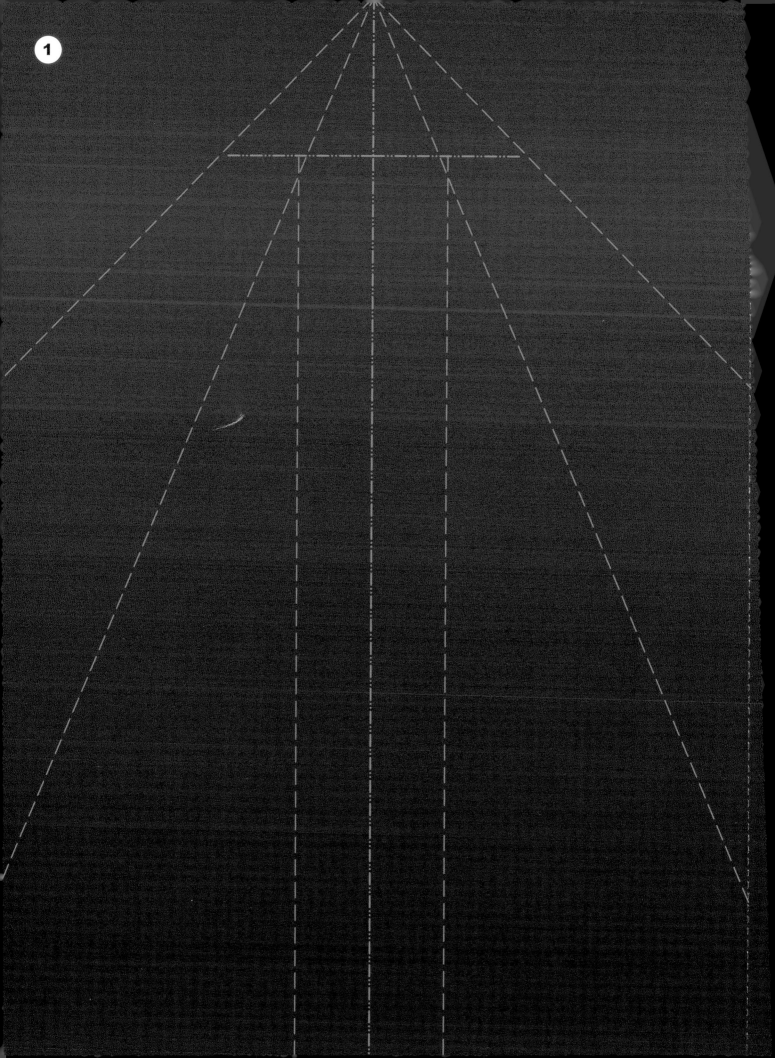

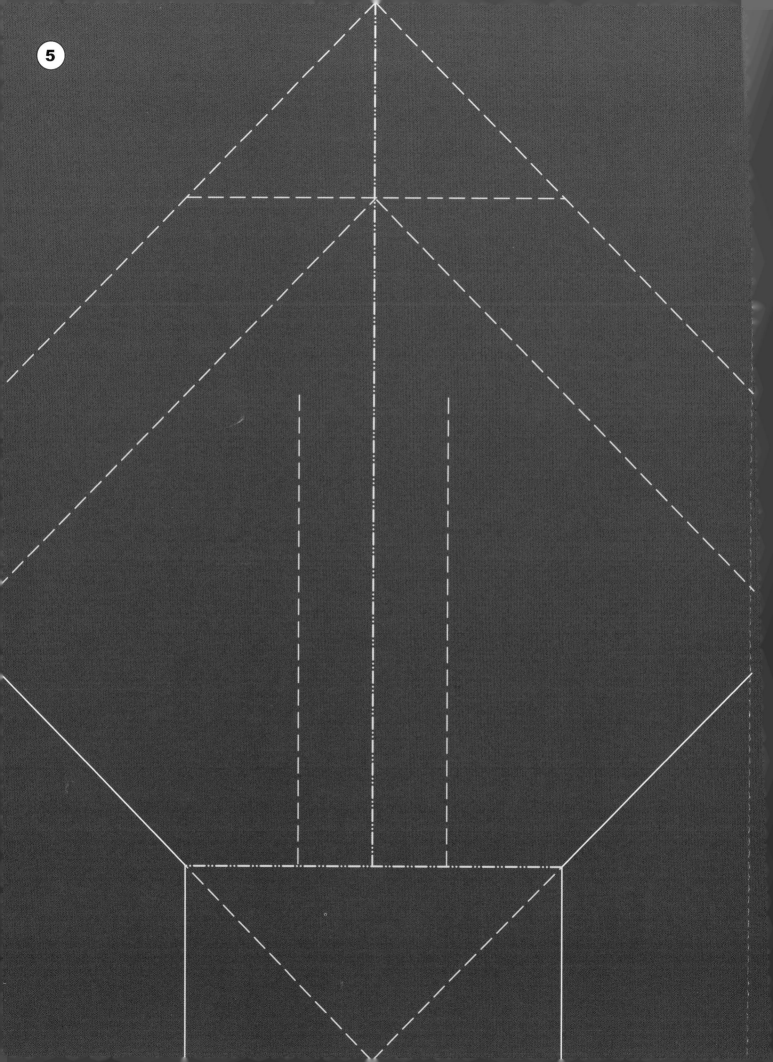

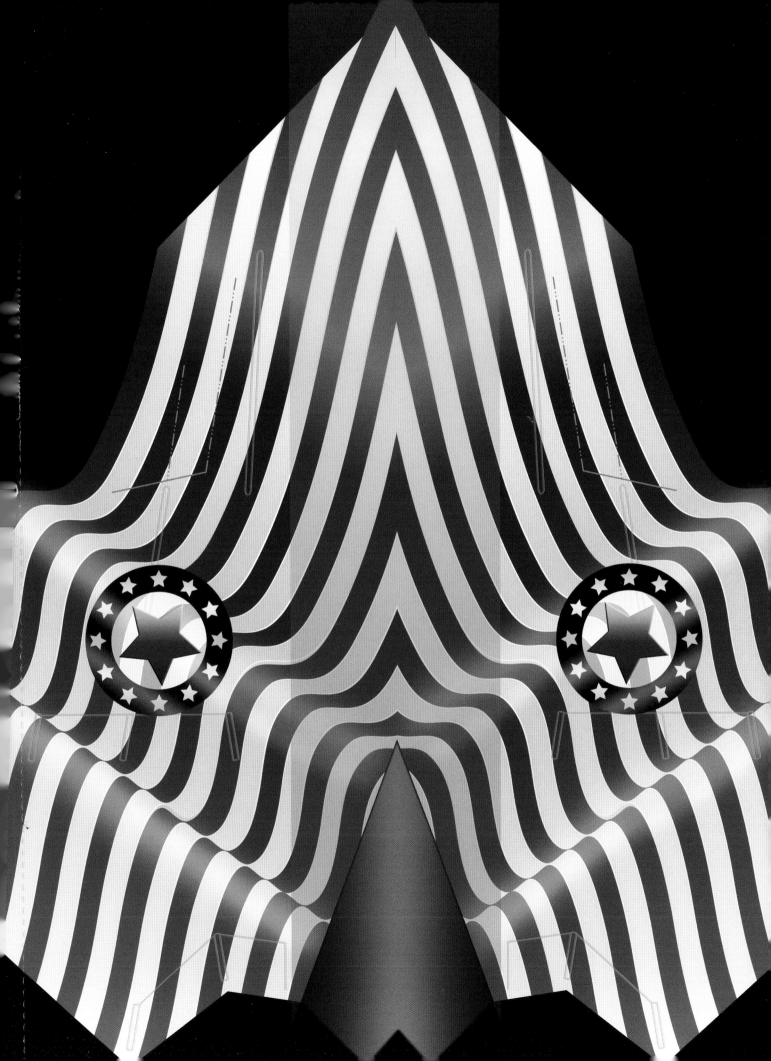

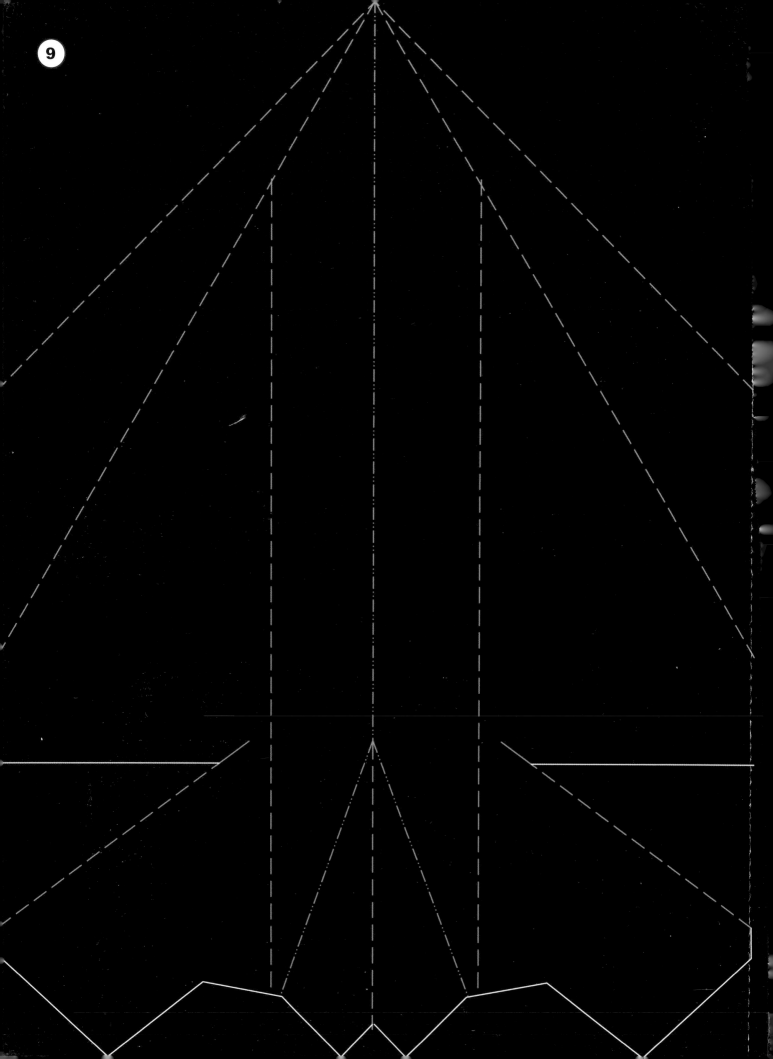